Contents

i

Trace the letter. Then circle the pictures whose names begin with the sound for the letter.

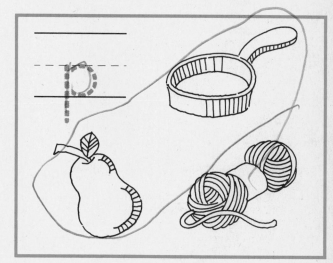

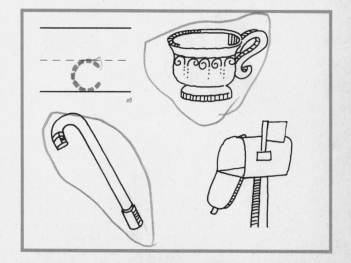

Name _____ 1

Say each picture name. Print the letter that stands for the beginning sound.

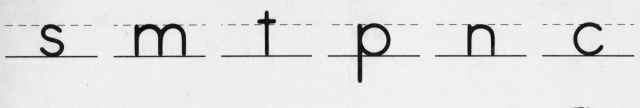

s m t p n c

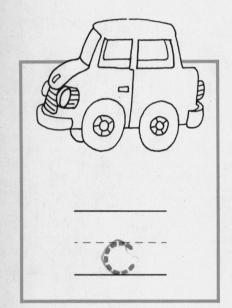

c

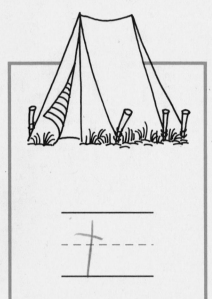

t

m

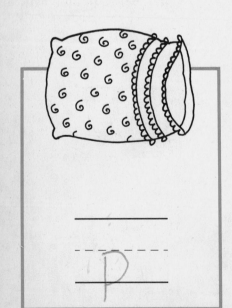

p

st

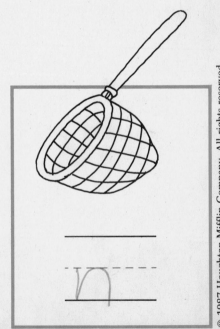

n

Phonics Home Activity: Hold this page where your child can't see it. Then say each picture name, and have your child name the letter that stands for the beginning sound. Ask your child to say another word that has the same beginning sound.

Trace the letter. Then circle the pictures whose
names begin with the sound for the letter.

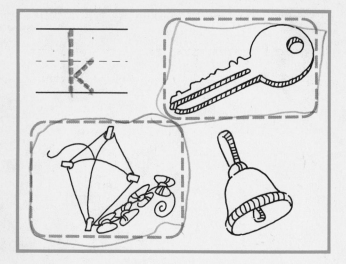

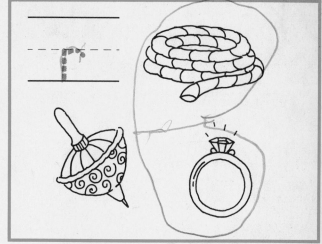

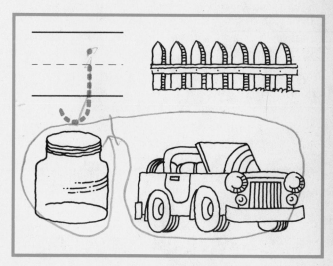

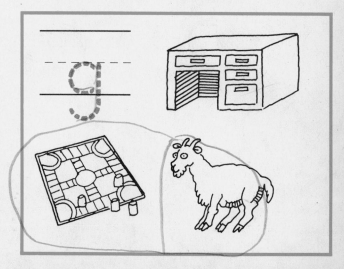

Name _____ 3

Say each picture name. Print the letter that stands
for the beginning sound.

k r b j f g

j

k

b

k

f

r

Phonics Home Activity: Hold this page where your child can't see it. Then say each picture name, and
have your child name the letter that stands for the beginning sound. Ask your child to say another word
that has the same beginning sound.

4

Trace the letter. Then circle the pictures whose names begin with the sound for the letter.

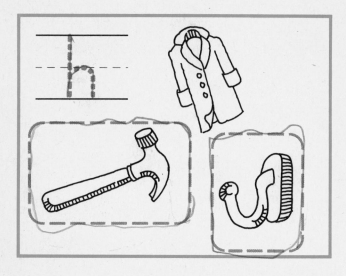

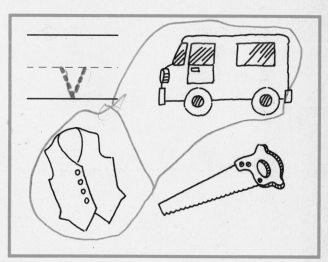

Name _____ 5

Say each picture name. Print the letter that stands for the beginning sound.

h d w v l y

l

d

v

h

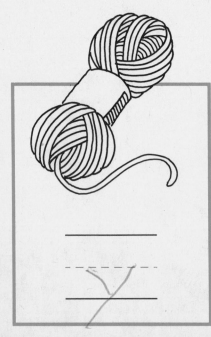

y

w

6

Phonics Home Activity: Hold this page where your child can't see it. Then say each picture name, and have your child name the letter that stands for the beginning sound. Ask your child to say another word that has the same beginning sound.

Say each picture name. Fill in the circle next to the
letter that stands for the beginning sound.

★ ○ v
　○ f
　○ h

1. ○ l
　 ○ w
　 ○ k

2. ○ s
　 ○ g
　 ○ n
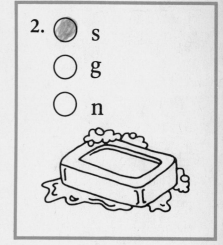

3. ○ j
　 ○ p
　 ○ g
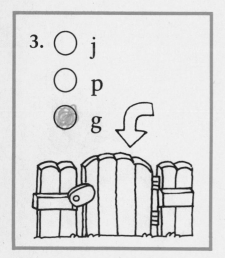

4. ○ b
　 ○ v
　 ○ t

5. ○ m
　 ○ r
　 ○ d
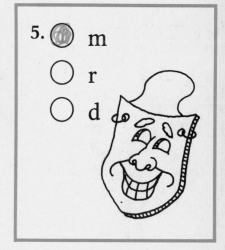

6. ○ k
　 ○ b
　 ○ n

7. ○ h
　 ○ y
　 ○ s
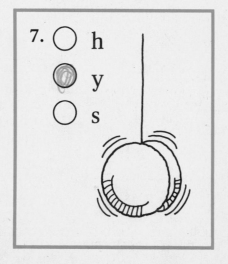

8. ○ w
　 ○ c
　 ○ p

Number right _____

Name _____

Say each picture name. Fill in the circle next to the letter that stands for the beginning sound.

★ ● r
○ l
○ j

1. ● k
   ○ m
   ○ f

2. ○ t
   ○ c
   ● h

3. ○ b
   ● c
   ○ m

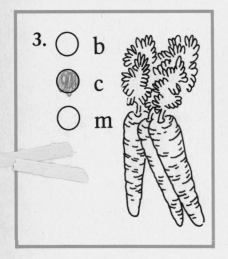

4. ● t
   ○ y
   ○ c

5. ○ w
   ○ l
   ● n

6. ○ s
   ○ g
   ● w

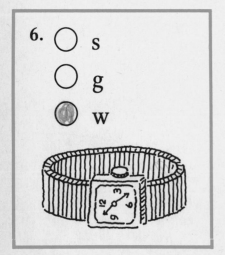

7. ● j
   ○ p
   ○ v

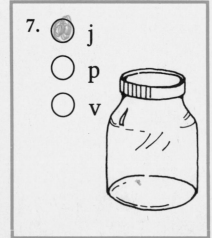

8. ○ f
   ● d
   ○ l

Number right _____

Phonics Home Activity: Hold this page where your child can't see it and name the pictures. Ask your child to tell you what letter each picture name begins with. Then ask your child to say a word that begins with the sound for each of the other letters on the page.

Say each picture name. Circle each picture whose
name ends with the sound for *t*.

boat

Name _____

final **r/t**

Say each picture name. Print *t* if the picture name ends with the sound for *t*.

bo<u>a</u>t

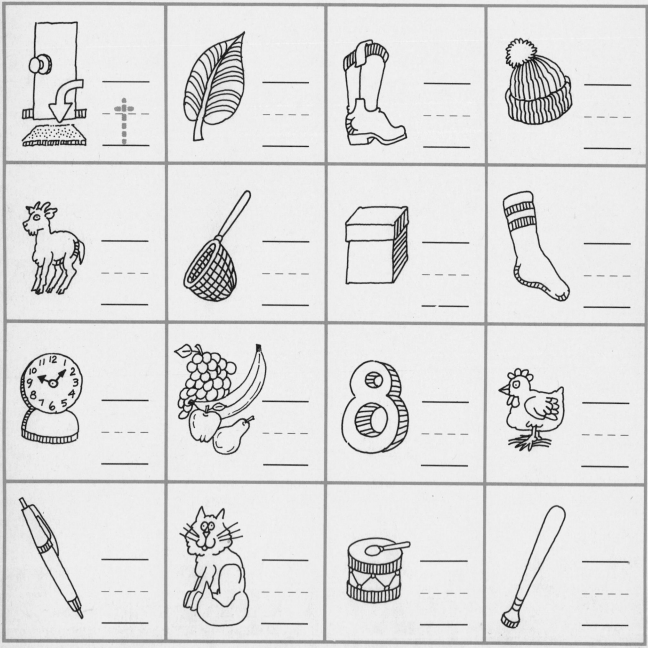

Phonics Home Activity: Help your child cut out all the pictures on this page whose names end with the sound for *t*. Then ask your child to paste these pictures onto a sheet of paper and print the letter *t* under each one.

Make each sentence tell about the picture. Circle the word you would use. Then print the word.

jet   jar   deer

1. I will go to a __jet__ .

bat   cat   car

2. I can help a _____ .

hammer   hat   bear

3. I can go to a _____ .

feet   dot   door

4. I will go to a _____ .

four   boat   foot

5. We will go to a _____ .

Name _____

check

Say each picture name. Fill in the circle next to the letter that stands for the ending sound.

★ ● r ○ t
1. ○ r ○ t
2. ○ r ○ t
3. ○ r ○ t
4. ○ r ○ t
5. ○ r ○ t
6. ○ r ○ t
7. ○ r ○ t

Fill in the circle next to the word that names the picture.

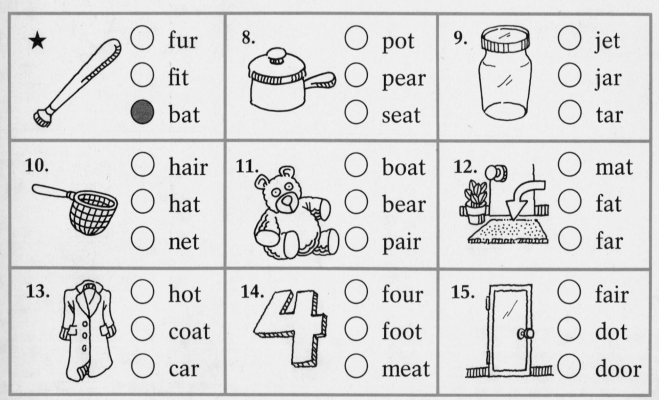

★ ○ fur ○ fit ● bat
8. ○ pot ○ pear ○ seat
9. ○ jet ○ jar ○ tar
10. ○ hair ○ hat ○ net
11. ○ boat ○ bear ○ pair
12. ○ mat ○ fat ○ far
13. ○ hot ○ coat ○ car
14. ○ four ○ foot ○ meat
15. ○ fair ○ dot ○ door

Number right _____

14 **Phonics Home Activity:** Hold this page where your child can't see it, and name each picture in the top section. Ask your child to tell what letter stands for the ending sound of each picture name. Then ask your child to tell which word names each picture in the bottom section.

Say each picture name. Circle each picture whose
name ends with the sound for *n*.

fa<u>n</u>

Name _____ **15**

Say each picture name. Print *n* if the picture name ends with the sound for *n*.

fan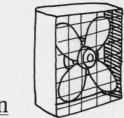

Phonics Home Activity: Ask your child to name all the pictures on this page and to tell which ones end with the sound for *n*. Then help your child cut from a magazine or newspaper pictures whose names end with the sound for *n*. Have your child paste these pictures onto a sheet of paper and print the letter *n* under each one.

Read each sentence. Circle the picture of the underlined word. Then print the word.

1. It will <u>run</u>.

_____

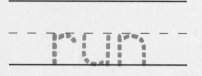

2. We will help a <u>man</u>.

_____
_ _ _ _ _ _ _ _
_____

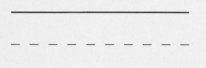   

3. You can get a <u>pen</u>.

_____
_ _ _ _ _ _ _ _
_____

4. We will go to a <u>van</u>.

_____
_ _ _ _ _ _ _ _
_____

5. I will get a <u>fan</u>.

_____
_ _ _ _ _ _ _ _
_____

Name _____

check

Say each picture name. Fill in the circle if the picture name ends with the sound for *n*.

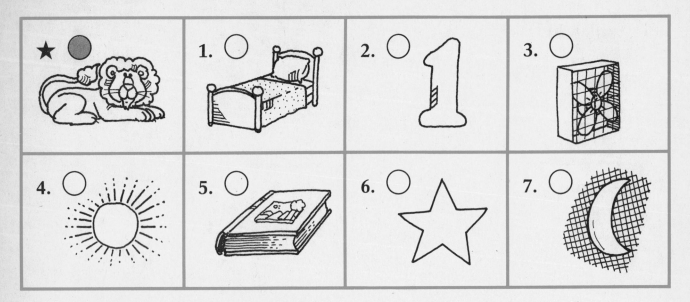

★ ●   1. ○   2. ○   3. ○

4. ○   5. ○   6. ○   7. ○

Say each picture name. Fill in the circle next to the word that names the picture.

★ ○ tin ○ pear ● pan	8. ○ hen ○ hut ○ fun	9. ○ tan ○ mat ○ moon
10. ○ bun ○ sat ○ sun	11. ○ cat ○ corn ○ horn	12. ○ pen ○ pot ○ ran
13. ○ van ○ fan ○ moon	14. ○ root ○ fun ○ rain	15. ○ man ○ top ○ ten

Number right _____

18

Phonics Home Activity: Hold this page where your child can't see it, and name each picture in the top section. Ask your child to tell whether the picture name ends with the sound for *n*. Then ask your child to tell which word names each picture in the bottom section.

Say each picture name. Circle each picture whose name begins with the sound for *th*.

<u>th</u>ermos

Name _____

Say each picture name. Print *th* if the picture name begins with the sound for *th*.

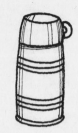

<u>th</u>ermos

<table>
<tr><td>th</td><td>_____</td><td>_____</td></tr>
</table>

Phonics Home Activity: Ask your child to name all the pictures on this page and to tell which ones begin with the sound for *th*. Then help your child cut from a magazine or newspaper pictures whose names begin with the sound for *th*. Have your child paste these pictures onto a sheet of paper and print *th* under each one.

Read each sentence. Circle the picture of the underlined word. Then print the word.

1. We will get <u>thirteen</u>.

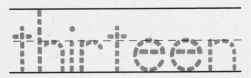   

2. You have a <u>thumb</u>.

3. You want a <u>thimble</u>.

4. I will not get a <u>thorn</u>.

5. I want <u>thirty</u>.

Name _____

check

Say each picture name. Fill in the circle if the picture name begins with the sound for *th*.

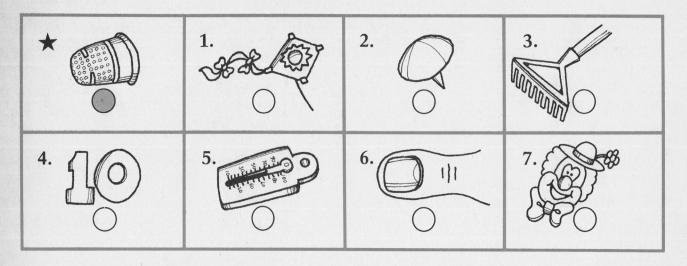

Fill in the circle next to the picture of the underlined word.

★ We want a <u>thimble</u>.

8. I have a <u>thermos</u>.

9. I have a <u>thumb</u>.

10. I do not want a <u>thorn</u>.

Number right _____

Phonics Home Activity: Hold this page where your child can't see it, and name each picture in the top section. Ask your child whether the picture name begins with the sound for *th*. Then have your child read each sentence at the bottom of the page and point to the picture of the underlined word.

Say each picture name. Circle each picture whose name ends with the sound for *d*.

be<u>d</u>

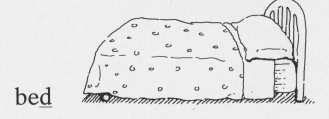

Name _____

final **d / k**

Say each picture name. Print *d* if the picture name ends with the sound for *d*.

be<u>d</u>

	d	

Phonics Home Activity: Say the name of each picture on this page, and ask your child to tell whether it ends with the sound for *d*. Then ask your child to look in a newspaper or magazine and circle pictures of things whose names end with the sound for *d*.

Say each picture name. Circle each picture whose name ends with the sound for *k*.

boo<u>k</u>

Name _____ 25

Say each picture name. Print *k* if the picture name ends with the sound for *k*.

boo<u>k</u>

Phonics Home Activity: Help your child cut out all the pictures on this page whose names end with the sound for *k*. Then ask your child to paste these pictures onto a sheet of paper and print the letter *k* under each one.

Make each sentence tell about the picture. Circle the word you would use. Then print the word.

mad   (sad)   look

1. I am ___sad___ .

bead   cook   book

2. I am a _____ .

hood   book   hook

3. You have a _____ .

pad   book   road

4. Here is a _____ .

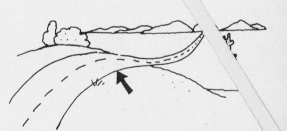

bed   book   red

5. I am in _____ .

Name _____   27

Say each picture name. Fill in the circle next to the letter that stands for the ending sound.

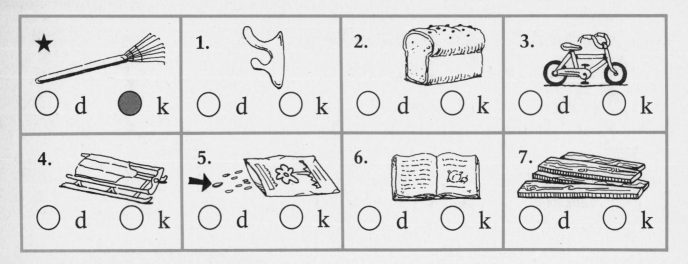

★ ○ d ● k

1. ○ d ○ k

2. ○ d ○ k

3. ○ d ○ k

4. ○ d ○ k

5. ○ d ○ k

6. ○ d ○ k

7. ○ d ○ k

Read each sentence. Fill in the circle next to the picture of the underlined word.

★ I want a <u>hood</u>.

8. It is a <u>road</u>.

9. Can you get a <u>book</u>?

10. Here is a <u>bed</u>.

Number right _____

28 **Phonics Home Activity:** Ask your child to tell what letter stands for the ending sound of each picture name in the top section, and to read the completed sentences at the bottom of the page. Then have your child choose two of the sentences to copy and illustrate on a separate sheet of paper.

Say each picture name. Circle each picture whose name ends with the sound for g.

dog

Name _____

29

final **g**

Say each picture name. Print *g* if the picture name
ends with the sound for *g*.

dog

	g	

Phonics Home Activity: Ask your child to name all the pictures on this page and to tell which ones end
with the sound for *g*. Then help your child cut from a magazine or newspaper pictures whose names end
with the sound for *g*. Have your child paste these pictures onto a sheet of paper and print the letter *g* under
each one.

Read each sentence. Circle the picture of the underlined word. Then print the word.

1. We like to jog.

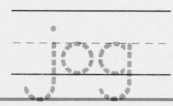   

2. I see the rag.

3. Here is a pig.

4. See the bug.

5. It is a big dog.

   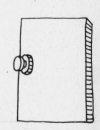

Name _____

Say each picture name. Fill in the circle if the picture name ends with the sound for *g*.

★	1.	2.	3.
4.	5.	6.	7.

Read each sentence. Fill in the circle next to the picture of the underlined word.

★ Here is the <u>log</u>.

8. Find the <u>dog</u>.

9. I see the <u>pig</u>.

10. The <u>rug</u> is in the home.

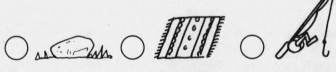

Number right _____

Phonics Home Activity: Have your child name the pictures in the top section that end with the sound for *g*. Then ask your child to read the sentences at the bottom of the page. Help your child list things in your home that contain the sound for *g*.

Say each picture name. Circle each picture whose name begins with the sounds for *fl*.

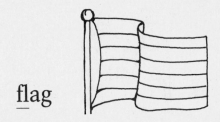

flag

Circle each picture whose name begins with the sounds for *fr*.

frog

Name _____

fl/fr

Print *fl* if the picture name begins with the sounds
for *fl*.

<u>fl</u>ag

Print *fr* if the picture name begins with the sounds
for *fr*.

<u>fr</u>og

Phonics Home Activity: Ask your child to cut out the pictures in the top section whose names begin with
the sounds for *fl* and to cut out the pictures in the bottom section whose names begin with the sounds for *fr*.
Then ask your child to paste these pictures onto a sheet of paper and print the letters *fl* or *fr* under each one.

Make each sentence tell about the picture. Circle the word you would use. Then print the word.

fruit   flag   (float)

1. I like to _float_ .

fruit   fled   flute

2. This is _____ .

freezer   from   flower

3. Here is a _____ for you.

flag   frog   frown

4. This is a _____ .

flood   flame   frame

5. It is a big _____ .

Name _____

check

Say each picture name. Fill in the circle next to the letters that stand for the beginning sounds.

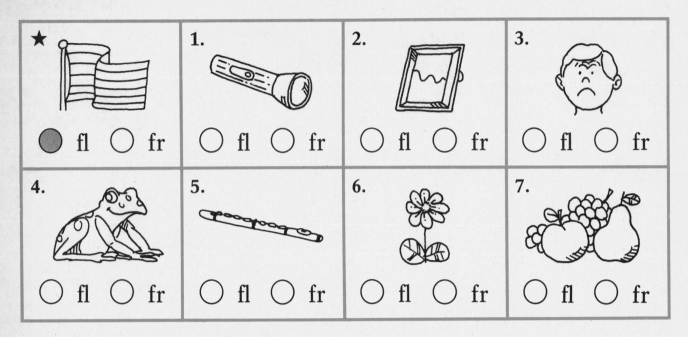

★ ● fl ○ fr   1. ○ fl ○ fr   2. ○ fl ○ fr   3. ○ fl ○ fr

4. ○ fl ○ fr   5. ○ fl ○ fr   6. ○ fl ○ fr   7. ○ fl ○ fr

Read each sentence. Fill in the circle next to the picture the sentence tells about.

★ I can <u>fry</u> it.

8. Where is the <u>flag</u>?

9. I see a <u>frog</u>.

10. The <u>floor</u> is in your home.

Number right _____

Phonics Home Activity: Hold this page where your child can't see it. Then name each picture in the top section, and ask your child to tell what letters stand for the beginning sounds. Ask your child to read the sentences at the bottom of the page.

Say each picture name. Circle each picture whose name ends with the sounds for *x*.

box

Name _____

37

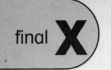

Say each picture name. Print *x* if the picture name ends with the sounds for *x*.

bo<u>x</u>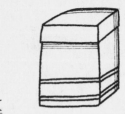

x		

Phonics Home Activity: Say the name of each picture on this page, and ask your child to tell whether it ends with the sounds for *x*. Then have your child color those pictures whose names end with the sounds for *x*.

Read each sentence. Circle the picture of the
underlined word. Then print the word.

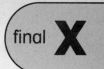

1. This is a big ox.

   _____

2. I see a little fox.

   _____

   _____

3. Where is my ax?

   _____

   _____

4. I will make a six.

   _____

   _____

5. What is in the box?

   _____

   _____

  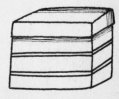

Name _____

Say each picture name. Fill in the circle if the picture name ends with the sounds for *x*.

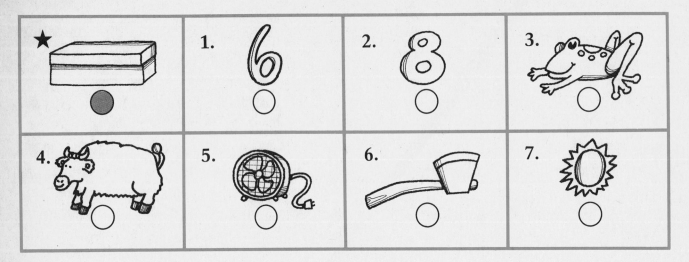

Read each sentence. Fill in the circle next to the picture of the underlined word.

★ I will <u>mix</u> this.

8. See the <u>fox</u>.

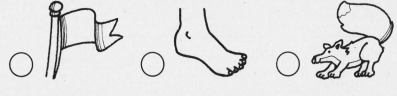

9. Where is the <u>six</u>?

10. Is the <u>box</u> for me?

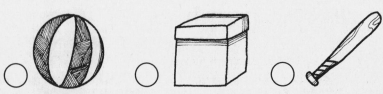

Number right _____

Phonics Home Activity: Hold this page where your child can't see it, and name each picture in the top section. Ask your child to tell whether or not the picture name ends with the sounds for *x*. Then have your child read the sentences at the bottom of the page.

Say each picture name. Circle each picture whose name ends with the sound for *th*.

teeth

Name _____ 41

Say each picture name. Print *th* if the picture name ends with the sound for *th*.

tee<u>th</u>

---

42 **Phonics Home Activity:** Help your child cut out all the pictures on this page whose names end with the sound for *th*. Then ask your child to paste these pictures onto a sheet of paper and print *th* under each one.

Read each sentence. Circle the picture the sentence tells about. Then print the underlined word.

1. It will get a <u>bath</u>.

2. I can see the <u>math</u>.

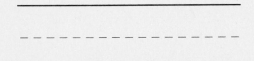   

3. Where is the <u>path</u>?

4. The <u>moth</u> is little.

5. Do you see the <u>teeth</u>?

Name _____

check

Say each picture name. Fill in the circle if the picture name ends with the sound for *th*.

Read each sentence. Fill in the circle next to the picture of the underlined word.

★ Here is a big <u>moth</u>.

8. It is not my <u>tooth</u>.

9. I see a little <u>path</u>.

10. Where is your <u>mouth</u>?

Number right _____

Phonics Home Activity: Ask your child to tell which picture names end with the sound for *th*, and to read the sentences at the bottom of the page. Then have your child choose two of the sentences to copy and illustrate on a separate sheet of paper.

Say each picture name. Circle each picture whose name <u>begins</u> with the sound for *ch*.

<u>ch</u>air

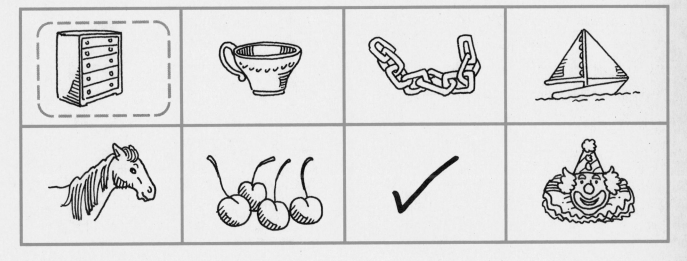

Circle each picture whose name <u>ends</u> with the sound for *ch*.

pea<u>ch</u>

initial
final **ch**

Say each picture name. Print *ch* if the picture name begins with the sound for *ch*.

chair

Print *ch* if the picture name ends with the sound for *ch*.

pea<u>ch</u>

46

Phonics Home Activity: Ask your child to name all the pictures on this page and to tell which ones begin with the sound for *ch* (top) or end with the sound for *ch* (bottom). Then help your child cut from a magazine or newspaper pictures whose names begin or end with the sound for *ch*. Have your child paste these pictures onto a sheet of paper and print *ch* under each one.

Read each sentence. Circle the picture the sentence
tells about. Then print the underlined word.

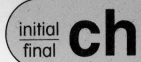

1. This is my <u>chin</u>.

chin

2. I will get a <u>peach</u>.

3. We like the <u>beach</u>.

4. Is this your <u>chair</u>?

5. I can make a <u>check</u>.

Name

check

Say each picture name. Fill in the circle if the picture name <u>begins</u> with the sound for *ch*.

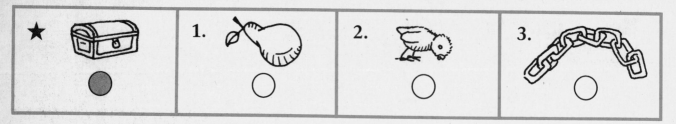

Fill in the circle if the picture name <u>ends</u> with the sound for *ch*.

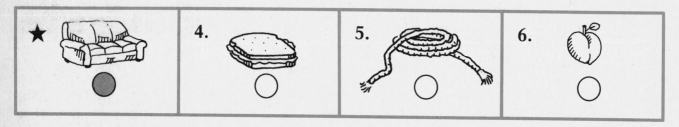

Read each sentence. Fill in the circle next to the picture of the underlined word.

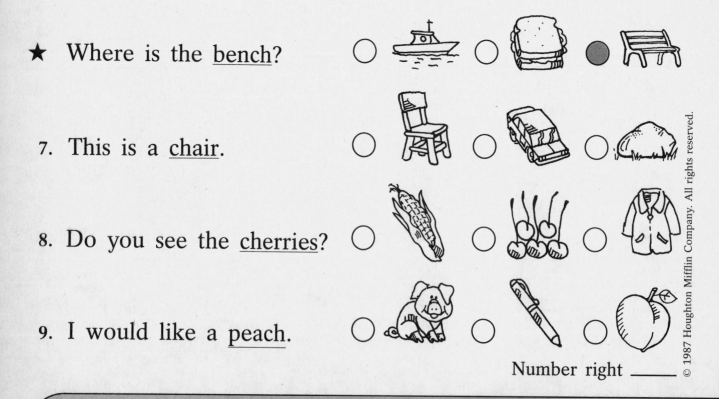

★ Where is the <u>bench</u>?

7. This is a <u>chair</u>.

8. Do you see the <u>cherries</u>?

9. I would like a <u>peach</u>.

Number right _____

48 **Phonics Home Activity:** Hold this page where your child can't see it, and name each picture in the boxes. Ask your child if the picture name begins with the sound for *ch* (first row) or ends with the sound for *ch* (second row). Then ask your child to read the sentences at the bottom of the page.

Say each picture name. Circle each picture whose
name ends with the sound for *p*.

to**p**

Name _____

final **p**

Say each picture name. Print *p* if the picture name
ends with the sound for *p*.

to**p**

Phonics Home Activity: Say the name of each picture on this page, and ask your child to tell whether it
ends with the sound for *p*. Then ask your child to look in a newspaper or magazine and circle pictures of
things whose names end with the sound for *p*.

Read each sentence. Circle the picture of the underlined word. Then print the word.

1. Look at the <u>map</u>.

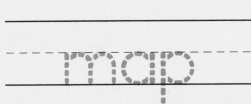   

2. Where is the <u>cup</u>?

3. You can <u>chop</u> this.

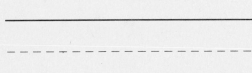   

4. I have on a <u>cap</u>.

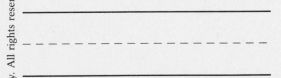  

5. Where is the <u>pup</u>?

   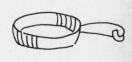

Name _____

check

Say each picture name. Fill in the circle if the picture name ends with the sound for *p*.

★ 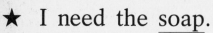 ●	1. 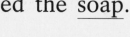 ◯	2.  ◯	3.  ◯
4. 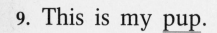 ◯	5. 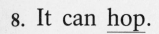 ◯	6. ◯	7. ◯

Read each sentence. Fill in the circle next to the picture of the underlined word.

★ I need the <u>soap</u>. ◯  ◯   ●

8. It can <u>hop</u>. ◯  ◯  ◯

9. This is my <u>pup</u>. ◯  ◯ 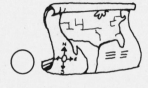 ◯

10. I have a <u>mop</u>. ◯  ◯  ◯

Number right _____

Phonics Home Activity: Hold this page where your child can't see it, and name each picture in the top section. Ask your child to tell whether or not the picture name ends with the sound for *p*. Then have your child read the sentences at the bottom of the page.

Say each picture name. Circle each picture whose
name has the short *a* sound.

apple   cat

Name _____ **53**

Say each picture name. Circle each picture whose name has the short *a* sound.

<u>a</u>pple   c<u>a</u>t

54 **Phonics Home Activity:** Help your child cut out all the pictures on this page whose names contain the short a sound. Then ask your child to paste these pictures onto a sheet of paper and print the letter a under each one.

Say each picture name. Print *a* if the picture name
has the short *a* sound.

apple

cat

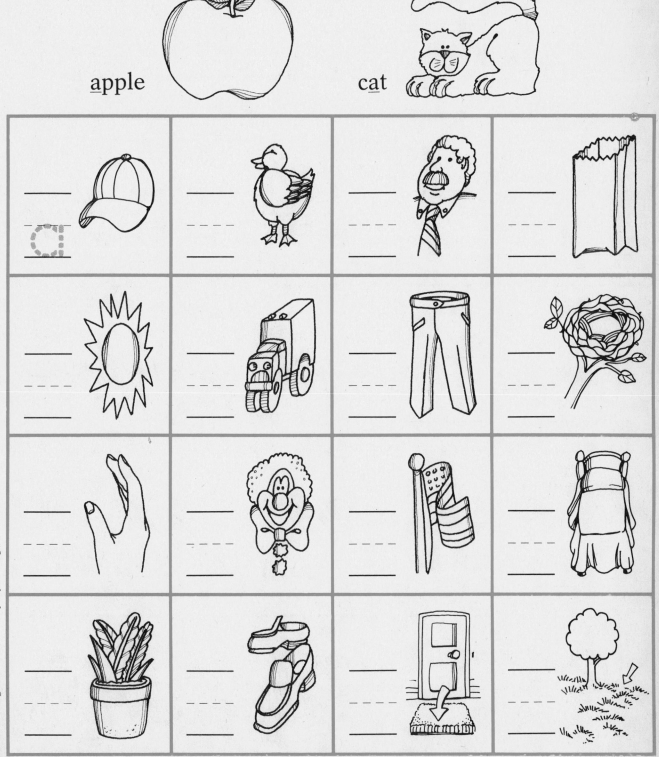

Name _____

Read each sentence. Circle the picture of the
underlined word. Then print the word.

1. Look at my <u>bat</u>.

2. What is a <u>fan</u>?

3. There is my <u>cap</u>.

4. That thing is a <u>pan</u>.

5. There is the <u>bag</u>.

 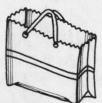  

Phonics Home Activity: Ask your child to read each sentence and to point to the picture of the underlined word. Then, on another sheet of paper, help your child write a few of the underlined words without looking at them.

Circle the word that completes the sentence. Then print the word.

1. I will get the ___map___ .

sad

(map)

bad

2. A father is a _____ .

wax

had

dad

3. We will _____ the cat.

pat

sat

flat

4. You _____ home.

sad

ran

path

5. We will go on this _____ .

bad

path

ran

Name _____

Say each picture name. Fill in the circle if you hear the short *a* sound.

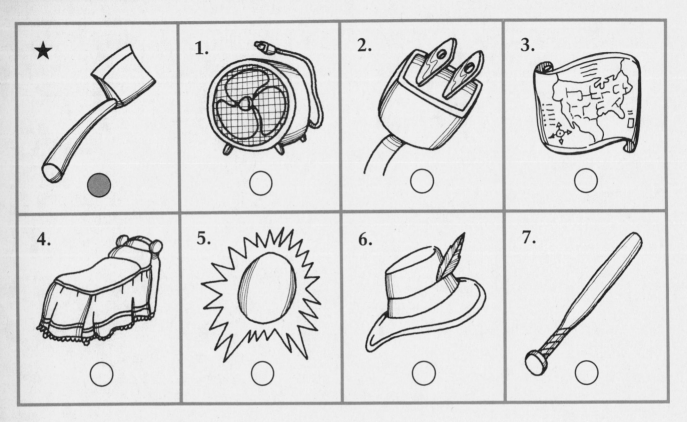

Fill in the circle next to the word that completes each sentence.

★ Where is the _____ ?
  ○ mad   ○ sat   ● flag

8. I _____ fun.
  ○ had   ○ man   ○ van

9. The hat is on the _____ .
  ○ bad   ○ fat   ○ man

10. The cat is on my _____ .
  ○ nap   ○ lap   ○ sat

Number right _____

Phonics Home Activity: Hold this page where your child can't see it, and name each picture in the top section. Ask your child to tell whether or not the picture name contains the short *a* sound. Then have your child read the completed sentences at the bottom of the page.

Say each picture name. Circle the picture if you
hear the long *a* sound.

apron   gate

Name _____   **59**

Say each picture name. Circle the picture if you hear the long *a* sound.

apron   gate

Phonics Home Activity: Say the name of each picture on this page, and ask your child to tell whether it contains the long *a* sound. Then ask your child to look in a newspaper or magazine and circle pictures of things whose names contain the long *a* sound.

Trace the letters *a* and final *e* to make the word *gate*.

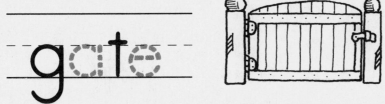

Print *a* and final *e* to complete each word. Then circle the picture the word names.

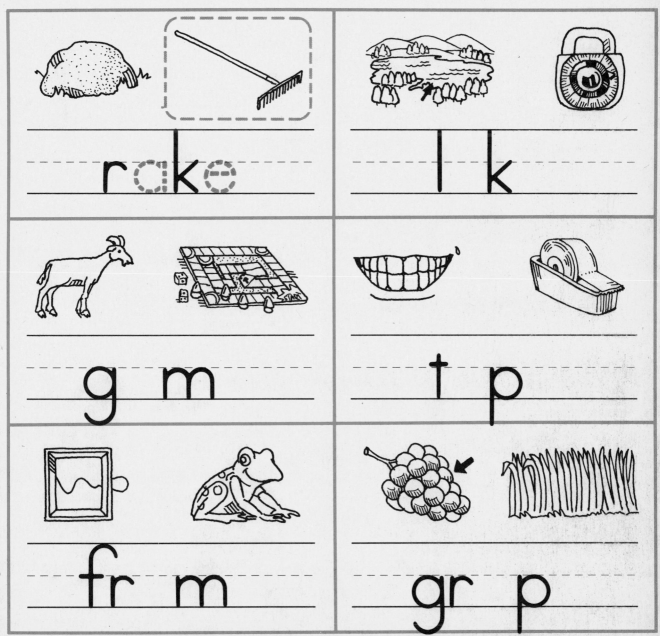

r a k e

l   k

g   m

t   p

f r   m

g r   p

Name _____

Read each sentence. Circle the picture of the
underlined word. Then print the word.

1. Where is my <u>cane</u>?

2. I put the <u>cape</u> on.

3. There is the <u>rake</u>.

4. Show me the <u>vase</u>.

5. We need the <u>tape</u>.

Phonics Home Activity: Ask your child to read each sentence and to point to the picture of the underlined word. Then, on another sheet of paper, help your child write a few of the underlined words without looking at them.

Circle the word that completes the sentence. Then print the word.

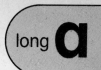

long **a**

came

(tape)

1. I will _____ **tape** _____ it.

lake

made

mane

2. I _____ my bed.

late

lake

same

3. You _____ me this pencil.

gave

sale

name

4. My _____ is Jed.

gate

game

save

5. This _____ is fun.

came

© 1987 Houghton Mifflin Company. All rights reserved.

Name _____ 63

check

Say each picture name. Fill in the circle if you hear the long *a* sound.

Fill in the circle next to the word that completes each sentence.

★ The book is for ____ .
  ○ wake   ● sale   ○ date

8. We have fun in the ____ .
  ○ gave   ○ late   ○ lake

9. We ____ home.
  ○ came   ○ frame   ○ gate

10. I will ____ some for you.
  ○ cane   ○ save   ○ game   Number right ____

Phonics Home Activity: Hold this page where your child can't see it, and name each picture in the top section. Ask your child to tell whether or not the picture name contains the long a sound. Then have your child read the completed sentences at the bottom of the page.

Say each picture name. Circle each picture whose name begins with the sounds for *br*.

b̲room

Name _____

br

Say each picture name. Print <u>br</u> if the picture name begins with the sounds for <u>br</u>.

<u>br</u>oom

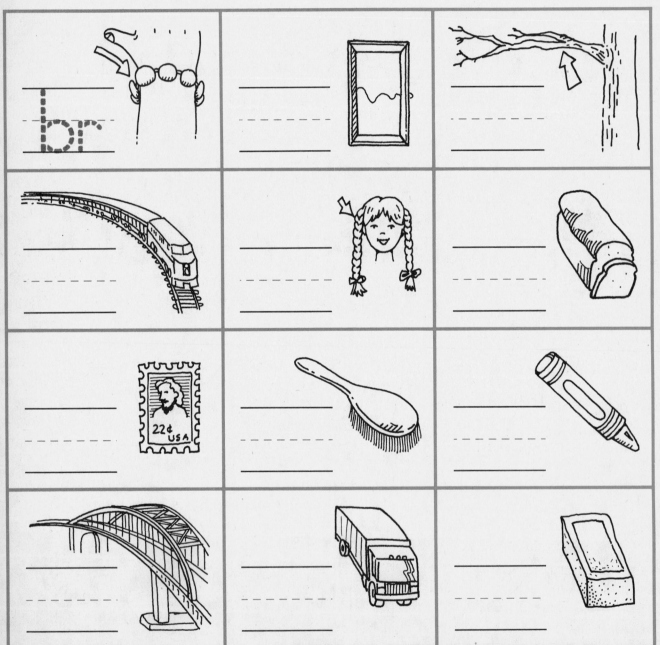

Phonics Home Activity: Help your child cut out all the pictures on this page whose names begin with the sounds for *br*. Then ask your child to paste these pictures onto a sheet of paper and print the letters *br* under each one.

Read each sentence. Circle the picture of the underlined word. Then print the word.

1. This is my broom.

  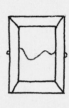 

2. I make my home with bricks.

3. The cat is on the branch.

4. Is that your bracelet?

5. Where is the bridge?

Name _____

check

Say each picture name. Fill in the circle if the
picture name begins with the sounds for *br*.

Read each sentence. Fill in the circle next to the
picture of the underlined word.

★ That is a big <u>branch</u>.

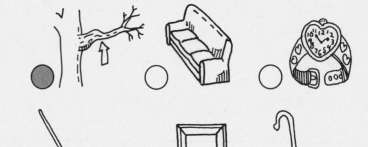

8. I have a <u>broom</u> at home.

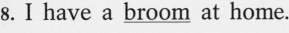

9. I like this <u>bread</u>.

10. This is a <u>brick</u>.

Number right _____

Phonics Home Activity: Ask your child to tell which picture names begin with the sounds for *br*, and to
read the sentences at the bottom of the page. Then have your child choose two of the sentences to
copy and illustrate on a separate sheet of paper.

Say each picture name. Circle each picture whose name begins with the sounds for *tr*.

tree

Circle each picture whose name begins with the sounds for *pl*.

plate

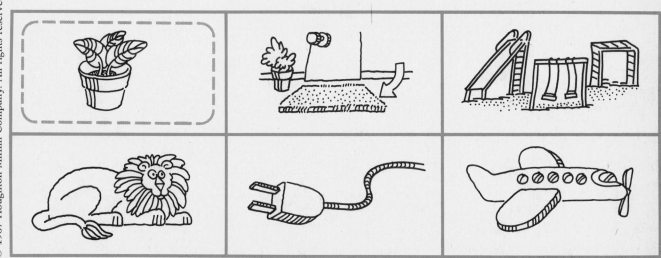

Name _____

Say each picture name. Print *tr* if the picture name begins with the sounds for *tr*.

<u>tr</u>ee

Print *pl* if the picture name begins with the sounds for *pl*.

<u>pl</u>ate

Phonics Home Activity: Ask your child to cut out the pictures in the top section whose names begin with the sounds for *tr* and to cut out the pictures in the bottom section whose names begin with the sounds for *pl*. Then ask your child to paste these pictures onto a sheet of paper and print the letters *tr* or *pl* under each one.

Make each sentence tell about the picture. Circle the word you would use. Then print the word.

trail   train   (plane)

1. Where will the _plane_ go?

trees   plows   plates

2. All the _____ are big.

truck   train   plum

3. We go on a _____ .

trap   plant   plug

4. This is a _____ .

plum   tray   plane

5. My lunch is on a _____ .

Say each picture name. Fill in the circle next to the letters that stand for the beginning sounds.

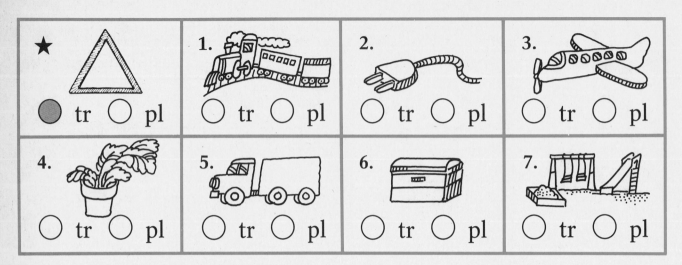

★ ● tr ○ pl
1. ○ tr ○ pl
2. ○ tr ○ pl
3. ○ tr ○ pl
4. ○ tr ○ pl
5. ○ tr ○ pl
6. ○ tr ○ pl
7. ○ tr ○ pl

Read each sentence. Fill in the circle next to the picture of the underlined word.

★ Where is the <u>plane</u>?

8. This <u>truck</u> is big.

9. It is on the <u>tracks</u>.

10. Here is the little <u>plant</u>.

Number right  _____

Phonics Home Activity: Hold this page where your child can't see it, and name each picture in the top section. Ask your child to tell what letters stand for the beginning sounds of each picture name. Then have your child read the sentences at the bottom of the page.

Say each picture name. Circle each picture whose
name has the sound for *c* that you hear in *cat*.

cat

Circle each picture whose name has the sound
for *c* that you hear in *city* and *face*.

c̲ity   fac̲e

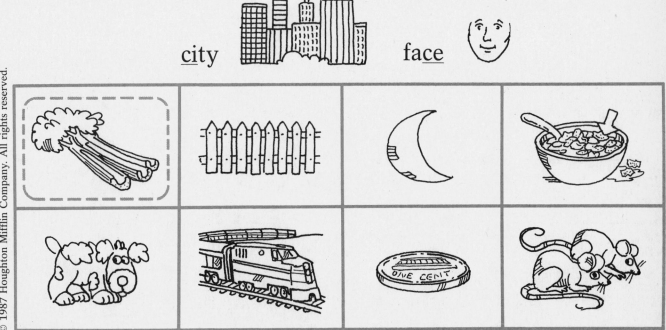

Name _____

Say each picture name. Circle the c and the letter that follows it in the name. Print the name in the correct column.

cup	mice	race
cape	cook	circle

city   face   cat

mice

cup

Houghton Mifflin Company. All rights reserved.

© 1987 Houghton Mifflin Company. All rights reserved.

74 **Phonics Home Activity:** Ask your child to read the word in each box and to tell what letter follows the c in the word. Then help your child read the words he or she wrote at the bottom of the page.

Read each sentence. Circle the picture of the underlined word. Then print the word.

1. Where are the <u>mice</u>?

_____

mice

2. I will have the <u>celery</u>.

_____

_____

3. This is one <u>coat</u>.

_____

_____

4. The <u>lettuce</u> is in the box.

_____

_____

5. This is a <u>circle</u>.

_____

_____

Name _____

Say each picture name. Fill in the circle if it has the sound for *c* that you hear in *city* and *face*.

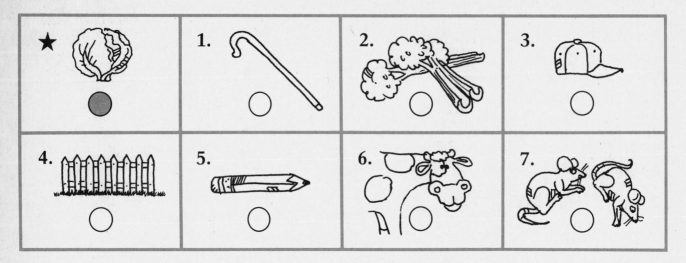

Read each sentence. Fill in the circle next to the picture of the underlined word.

★ I like <u>carrots</u>.

8. This is one <u>cent</u>.

9. Today I will see a <u>camel</u>.

 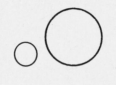 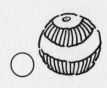

10. Where is the <u>race</u>?

Number right _____

76 **Phonics Home Activity:** Hold this page where your child can't see it, and name the pictures in the top section. Have your child tell you if the picture name contains the sound for *c* that you hear in *city* and *face*. Then ask your child to read the sentences at the bottom of the page.

Say each picture name. Circle each picture whose name <u>begins</u> with the sounds for *st*.

<u>st</u>ar

Circle each picture whose name <u>ends</u> with the sounds for *st*.

toa<u>st</u>

Name _____

Say each picture name. Print *st* if the picture name begins with the sounds for *st*.

star

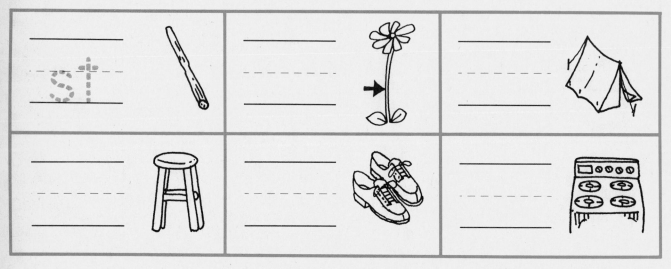

Print *st* if the picture name ends with the sounds for *st*.

toa<u>st</u>

Phonics Home Activity: Ask you child to name all the pictures on this page and to tell which ones begin with the sounds for *st* (top) or end with the sounds for *st* (bottom). Then have your child color those pictures whose names begin or end with the sounds for *st*.

Read each sentence. Circle the picture of the
underlined word. Then print the word.

1. I need a <u>stamp</u>.

2. I have a <u>vest</u>.

3. Where is the <u>store</u>?

4. This is a little <u>stone</u>.

5. We have a <u>list</u>.

Name _____

check

Say each picture name. Fill in the circle if the picture name <u>begins</u> with the sounds for *st*.

Fill in the circle if the picture name <u>ends</u> with the sounds for *st*.

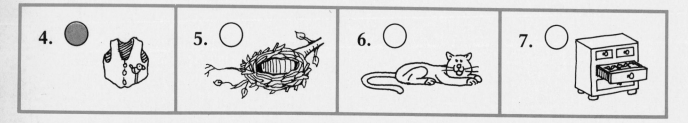

Read each sentence. Fill in the circle next to the picture of the underlined word.

★ I can't find the <u>stick</u>.

 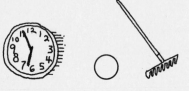

8. It is on the <u>step</u>.

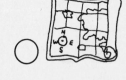  

9. Where is the <u>nest</u>?

10. What is in the <u>chest</u>?

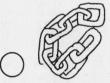  

Number right _____

Phonics Home Activity: Hold this page where your child can't see it, and name each picture in the boxes. Ask your child if the picture name begins with the sounds for *st* (first row) or ends with the sounds for *st* (second row). Then ask your child to read the sentences at the bottom of the page.

80

Say each picture name. Circle each picture whose name <u>begins</u> with the sound for *sh*.

<u>sh</u>oe

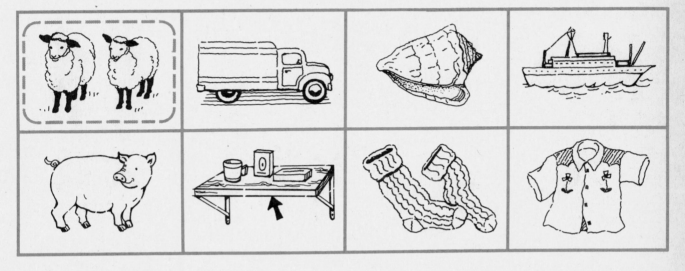

Circle each picture whose name <u>ends</u> with the sound for *sh*.

fi<u>sh</u>

Name _____

Say each picture name. Print *sh* if the picture name <u>begins</u> with the sound for *sh*.

<u>sh</u>oe

Print *sh* if the picture name <u>ends</u> with the sound for *sh*.

fi<u>sh</u>

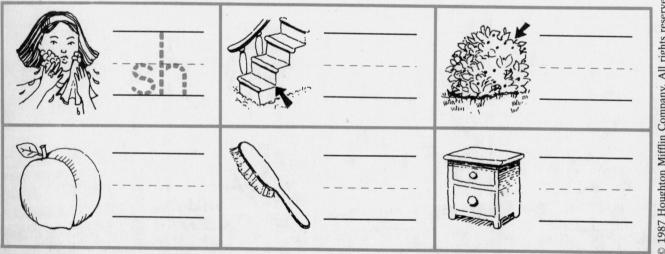

82 **Phonics Home Activity:** Ask your child to name all the pictures on this page and to tell which ones begin with the sound for *sh* (top) or end with the sound for *sh* (bottom). Then have your child look at a magazine and circle pictures of things whose names begin or end with the sound for *sh*.

Read each sentence. Circle the picture of the
underlined word. Then print the word.

1. I put my <u>shoes</u> on.

2. This is a big <u>bush</u>.

3. Where is the <u>fish</u>?

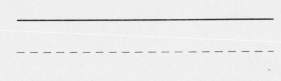

4. This is a nice <u>ship</u>.

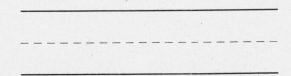

5. Thank you for the <u>shell</u>.

Name _____

check

Say each picture name. Fill in the circle if the picture name <u>begins</u> with the sound for *sh*.

| ★ ●  | 1. ○  | 2. ○  | 3. ○  |

Fill in the circle if the picture name <u>ends</u> with the sound for *sh*.

| ★ ●  | 4. ○  | 5. ○  | 6. ○  |

Read each sentence. Fill in the circle next to the picture of the underlined word.

★ There are the <u>sheep</u>.

7. Where is my <u>brush</u>?

8. I will put on my <u>shorts</u>.

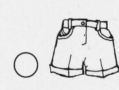 

9. Don't forget the <u>fish</u>.

Number right _____

Phonics Home Activity: Hold this page where your chiid can't see it, and name each picture in the boxes.
84 Ask your child if the picture name begins with the sound for *sh* (first row) or ends with the sound for *sh* (second row). Then ask your child to read the sentences at the bottom of the page.

Trace the letter at the end of the word. Then circle each picture whose name ends with the sound for that letter.

bear

cat

moon

Name _____

Say each picture name. Then print the letter that stands for the ending sound.

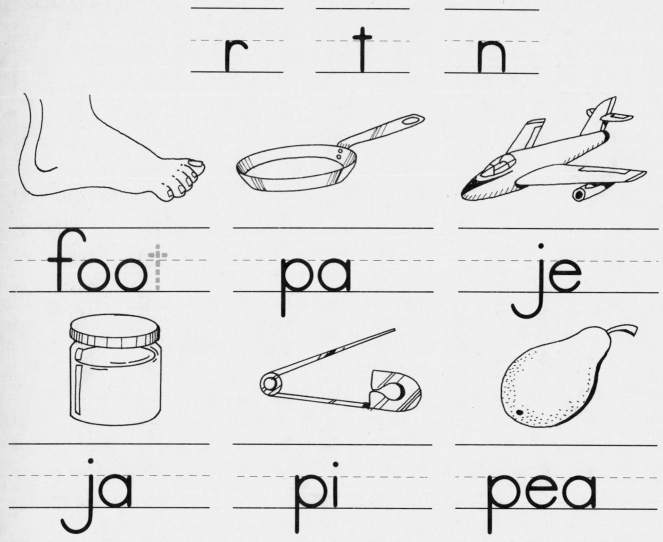

r   t   n

foo**t**   pa   je

ja   pi   pea

Circle the sentence that tells about the picture.

A cat will get it.

A man will get it.

Phonics Home Activity: Hold this page where your child can't see it, and name each picture in the top section. Ask your child to tell what letter stands for the ending sound of each picture name. Then have your child tell what is happening in the picture at the bottom of the page and read the sentence that goes with it.

Bear will go to one friend. To get there, Bear must walk only on pictures whose names begin with the sound for *th*. Draw a line that shows where Bear will go.

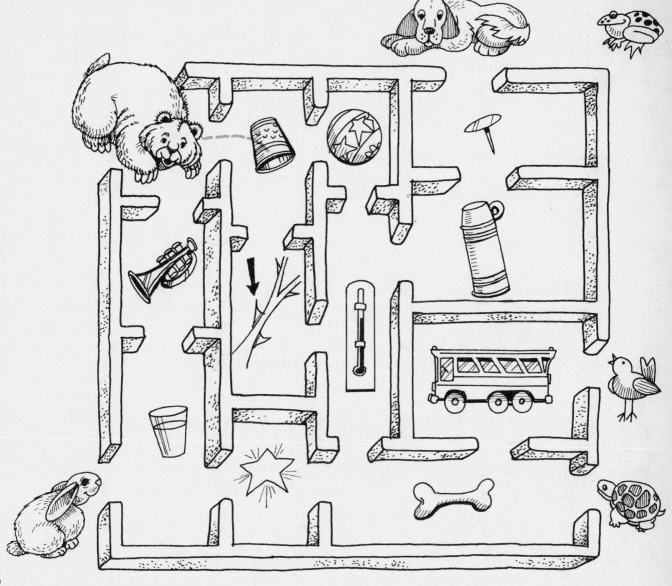

Circle the correct picture.

Bear will go to _____ .

Name _____

review

Trace the letter at the end of the word. Then circle each thing whose name ends with the sound for that letter.

road

book

dog

Phonics Home Activity: Have your child describe what he or she sees in the first picture. Then have your child color each thing in the picture whose name ends with the sound for *d*. Repeat this activity for the letters *k* and *g*.

Say each picture name. Then print the letter that stands for the ending sound.

d   k   g

book   clou   fla

ru   ya   brea

Circle the sentence that tells about the picture.

Here is a bat.

Here is a bag.

Read each sentence. Then name the picture.
Print the picture name next to the sentence number
in the puzzle.

book   bat   thorn   barn

1. I have a ____ .

2. See the big ____ .

3. Do you see a ____ ?

4. Here is the ____ .

1 b	a	2 t
3		
4		

brook   bag   bread

1. The ____ is good.

2. I think it is a ____ .

3. Would you find the ____ ?

1		
2		
3		

Phonics Home Activity: Have your child read each completed sentence on this page and show where the word belongs in the crossword puzzle. Then ask your child to choose one of the sentences to copy and illustrate on another sheet of paper.

Circle each picture name. Then print the words
where they belong in the story.

(sun)   sad   bag   bat

_____

The _____ sun _____ did come out.

Now Cat can go out.

_____

- - - - - - - - - - - -

Cat will take the _____ .

Cat will have fun.

book   boat   dot   dog

_____

- - - - - - - - - - - -

The _____ would like help.

The bear will help.

_____

- - - - - - - - - - - -

The bear will get the _____ .

Name _____   91

Circle each picture name. Then print the words where they belong in the story.

cook (car)   tag   toad

_____

What is in the ____car____ ?

You can take a look.

What do you see in it?

_____

_____

You see a _____ in it!

---

4   13

four   five   ten   thirteen

Take a good look!

_____

_____

Cat is in the _____ !

_____

Bear is in the _____ !

Phonics Home Activity: Ask your child to read each story, inserting the words in the sentences completed on this page. Then have your child select one or more sentences to copy and illustrate on another sheet of paper.

Say each picture name. Fill in the circle next to the
letter that stands for the ending sound.

★
○ d
○ g
○ r

1.
○ g
○ n
○ t

2.
○ d
○ k
○ g

3.
○ t
○ n
○ r

4.
○ n
○ k
○ d

5.
○ t
○ g
○ r

6.
○ k
○ r
○ d

7.
○ g
○ t
○ k

8.
○ d
○ t
○ r

9.
○ k
○ g
○ n

10.
○ d
○ g
○ k

11.
○ g
○ r
○ k

12.
○ r
○ g
○ t

13.
○ g
○ d
○ t

14.
○ k
○ r
○ t

15.
○ k
○ t
○ r

Number right _____

Name _____

Read each sentence. Fill in the circle next to the picture of the underlined word.

★ It is a big <u>pot</u>.

1. Take the <u>book</u> home.

2. We can find the <u>road</u>.

3. We did not see a <u>deer</u>.

4. The <u>coat</u> is too big.

5. Did you see the <u>thorn</u>?

6. Here is the <u>tag</u>.

7. Did you take the <u>thermos</u>?

Number right _____

Phonics Home Activity: Ask your child to read each sentence and point to the picture of the underlined word. Then ask your child to make up a story using some of the underlined words on this page. Help your child write the story on a sheet of paper.

Say each picture name. Then print the letters that stand for the beginning sounds.

fl   fr

f ̲l̲ y   _ _ uit   _ _ ower

_ _ ame   _ _ ame   _ _ own

Circle the sentence that tells about the picture.

The little frog is for you.

The little flag is for you.

Name _____

Say the picture names. Listen for the ending sounds.
Print the letters that will finish the words.

_____ _____

x   th

a x   fo   ma

mo   too   bo

Make each sentence tell about the picture. Circle the
word you would use. Then print the word.

pan   path

_____

Take the _____ to the homes.

six   seven

_____

You will see _____ homes.

Phonics Home Activity: Hold this page where your child can't see it, and name each picture in the top
section. Ask your child to tell if the picture name ends with *x* or *th*. Then have your child read the completed
sentences at the bottom of the page.

Look at the picture. Circle the things whose names have the sound for *ch*. The sound can be at the beginning or the end.

Read each sentence. Circle the picture of the underlined word.

1. Did you find the chain?

 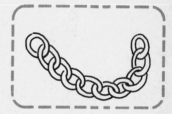

2. Did you find the sandwich?

3. Did you find the chair?

4. Did you find the bench?

 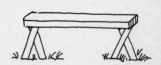

Name _____

review

This kite needs a tail. To make the tail, draw a line through each picture whose name ends with the sound for *p*.

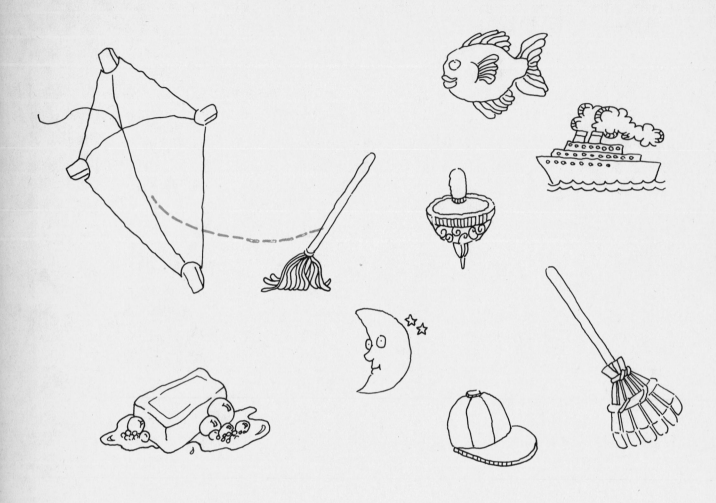

Read the sentences. Circle the word that is missing. Then print the word.

pig   pup

The kite can fly now.

_____

— — — — — — — — — —

The _____ will fly it.

98 **Phonics Home Activity:** Say the name of each picture in the top section of this page, and ask your child to tell whether it ends with the sound for *p*. Then ask your child to read the sentences at the bottom of the page.

Read each sentence. Then name the picture.
Print the picture name next to the sentence number
in the puzzle.

fruit   float

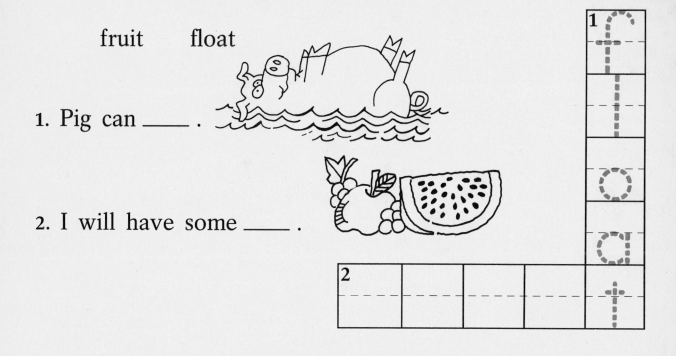

1. Pig can ____ .

2. I will have some ____ .

frame   flame

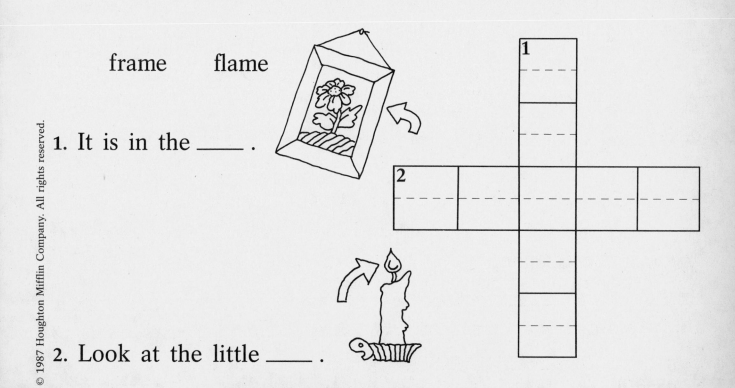

1. It is in the ____ .

2. Look at the little ____ .

Name _____

Make the sentences tell about the pictures.
Print the words where they belong.

mix   cup

Cat needs a _____ cup _____ .

Now Cat can _____ mix _____ it.

fix   jeep

Rabbit will get the _____ to go.

Turtle will help to _____ it.

soap   box

What do you think is in the _____ ?

It is animal _____ for Little Bear.

100 **Phonics Home Activity:** Have your child read the completed sentences on this page. Then, on another sheet of paper, help your child write and illustrate the words *cup* and *box*.

Read the sentences. Then do what the sentences tell you to do.

Find the <u>path</u>.
Make a rabbit in it.

Find the <u>chick</u>.
Make more chicks.

Find the little <u>peach</u>.
Make a big peach.

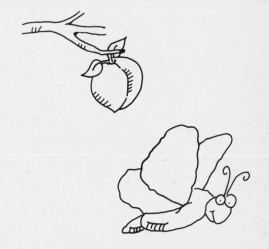

Find the <u>moth</u>.
Make a friend for it.

Find the <u>chair</u>.
Make it red.

Find the <u>couch</u>.
Make it like you want.

Name _____

Read each sentence. Find the picture of the underlined word. Then print the picture number beside the sentence.

1.

2.

3.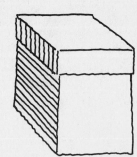

4.

5.

6.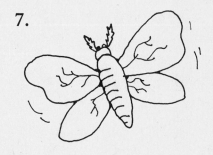

7.

Bear and the Surprises

Bear gets a big <u>box</u>. ___4___

Bear takes out a little <u>flag</u>. ___

It is for the <u>pup</u>. ___

Now Bear takes out some <u>fruit</u>. ___

It is for the <u>moth</u>. ___

Now Bear will surprise the <u>chick</u>. ___

Bear takes out a <u>sandwich</u>. ___

Bear is a good friend!

Phonics Home Activity: Help your child name the pictures at the top of this page and read the story. Then ask your child to choose one of the sentences in the story to copy and illustrate on another sheet of paper.

Say the picture names. Fill in the circles next to the letters that stand for the beginning sounds.

★
○ ch
● fl
○ fr

1.
○ ch
○ fl
○ fr

2.
○ ch
○ fl
○ fr

3.
○ ch
○ fl
○ fr

4.
○ ch
○ fl
○ fr

5.
○ ch
○ fl
○ fr

6.
○ ch
○ fl
○ fr

7.
○ ch
○ fl
○ fr

Fill in the circles next to the letters that stand for the ending sounds.

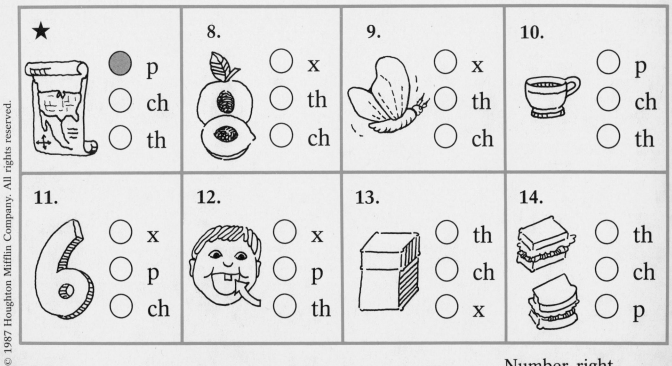

★
● p
○ ch
○ th

8.
○ x
○ th
○ ch

9.
○ x
○ th
○ ch

10.
○ p
○ ch
○ th

11.
○ x
○ p
○ ch

12.
○ x
○ p
○ th

13.
○ th
○ ch
○ x

14.
○ th
○ ch
○ p

Number right _____

Name _____

103

Read each sentence. Fill in the circle next to the picture of the underlined word.

★ Here is the <u>fruit</u>.

1. Is a frog in the <u>box</u>?

2. The <u>chain</u> is not red.

3. Do you see the <u>moth</u>?

4. I want to have a <u>peach</u>.

5. The <u>flag</u> is for you.

6. This is a <u>chick</u>.

7. The <u>pup</u> is little.

Number right _____

Say each picture name. Color the part red if the name has the short *a* sound. Color it blue if the name has the long *a* sound.

Name _____ 105

review

Draw a line from each picture to its name. Print the name in the **bag** if it has the short *a* sound. Print the name in the **frame** if it has the long *a* sound.

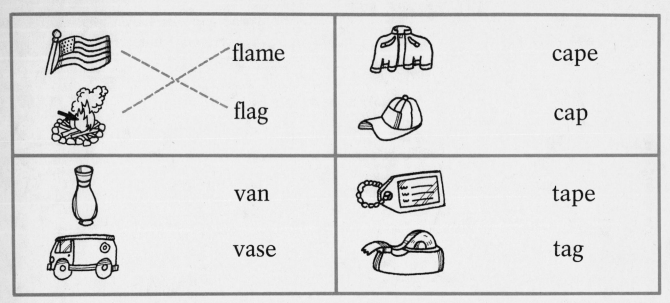

flame

flag

cape

cap

van

vase

tape

tag

bag

frame

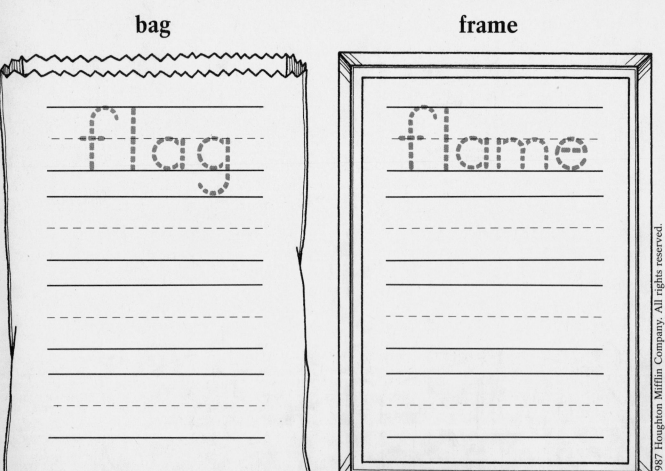

Phonics Home Activity: Ask your child to read each word in the top section and tell if it contains the short *a* sound or the long *a* sound. Then help your child write a few of these words without looking at them.

Trace the letters at the beginning of the word.
Then circle each picture whose name begins with
the sounds for those letters.

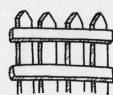
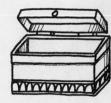

Name _____

Say each picture name. Print the letters that stand for the beginning sounds.

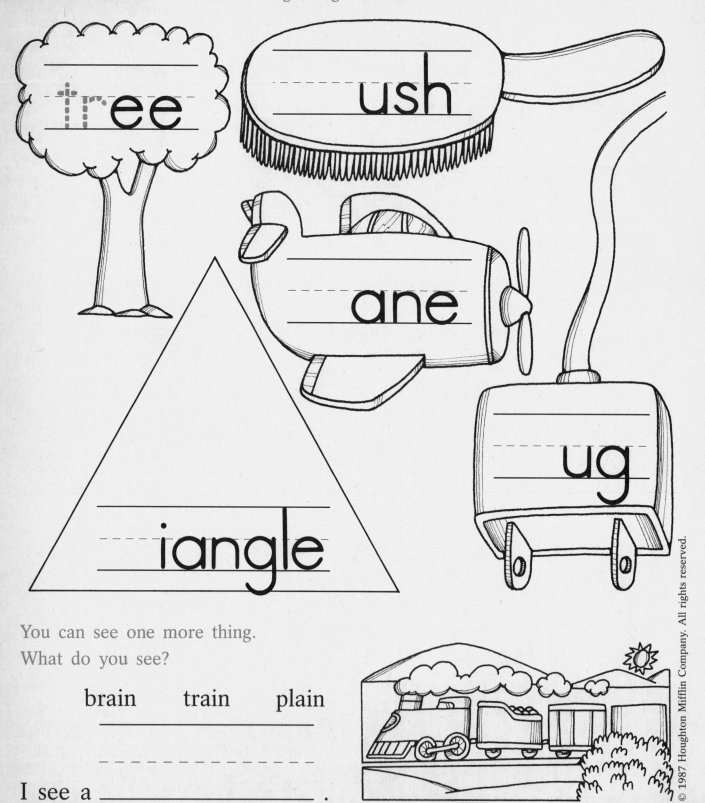

tree

ush

ane

ug

iangle

You can see one more thing.
What do you see?

brain   train   plain

I see a _____ .

Phonics Home Activity: Ask your child to name each picture in the top section and to tell which two letters stand for the beginning sounds in that name. Then have your child read the sentences at the bottom of the page.

The rabbits will go to two friends. They must walk
only on pictures whose names have the sound for *c*
that you hear in *face*. Draw a line to show where
the rabbits will go.

Where will the rabbits go?

_____

- - - - - - - - - - - - - -

They will go to the _____ .

turtles   mice   bears   cats

Name _____   109

Look at the picture. Circle each thing whose name has the sounds for *st*. The sound may be at the beginning or end.

Circle the picture of the underlined word. Then print *yes* or *no*.

Did you find the <u>list</u>?

_____

- - - - - - - - - - - - - - -

_____

Did you find the <u>star</u>?

_____

- - - - - - - - - - - - - - -

_____

Good for you!

Phonics Home Activity: Ask your child to tell what he or she sees in the big picture and read the sentences at the bottom of the page. Then have your child color the things in the big picture that contain the sounds for *st*.

Look at the picture. Circle the things whose names have the sound for *sh*. The sound may be at the beginning or end.

Circle the picture of the underlined word. Then print *yes* .or *no*.

Did you see a <u>fish</u>?

_____

— — — — — — — — — —

_____

You may make one.
Find a good place to put it.

Name _____

review

Read each sentence. Then name the picture. Print the picture name next to the sentence number in the puzzle.

train   plane   brush   trash

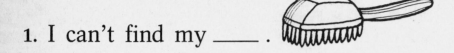

1. I can't find my ____ .

2. Mother takes a ____ to work.

3. Please take out the ____ .

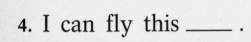

4. I can fly this ____ .

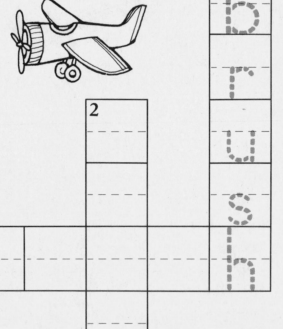

Phonics Home Activity: Have your child read the completed sentences on this page and show where each word belongs in the crossword puzzle. Then ask your child to copy and illustrate two of the words in the puzzle.

Read each sentence. Do what the sentence tells you to do.

1. Put a nose on the <u>face</u>.

 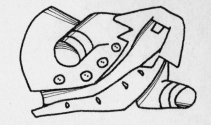

2. Make one more <u>cent</u>.

3. Make a rabbit to go with the <u>carrot</u>.

4. Make a little home for the <u>mice</u>.

5. Make the <u>car</u> red.

6. Put a nice hat on the <u>camel</u>.

Name _____

review Read the sentence. Look at the picture. Then print the missing words where they make sense.

store   nest

_____   _____

1. I see a ____nest____ on the ____store____ .

star   list

make lunch
☆ take book
bring cat in

_____   _____

2. Why is the _____ on the _____ ?

vest   stool

_____   _____

3. The _____ is on the _____ .

stove   toast

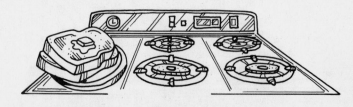

_____   _____

4. The _____ is on the _____ .

Read each sentence. Then name the picture. Print the picture name next to the sentence number in the puzzle.

shirt   brush

1. Where is my ____ ?

2. The ____ is on the bed.

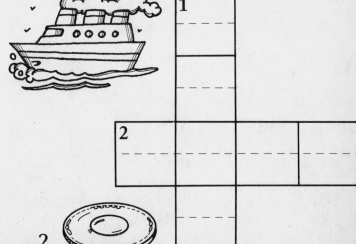

dish   ship

1. He will get a nice ____ .

2. Why do you have that ____ ?

Name _____

115

Read the sentences. Look at the picture. Do what the sentences tell you to do.

Find the <u>mat</u>.
Put a <u>plate</u> on it.

There is no <u>vase</u>!
Make one.

Fox needs a <u>bat</u>.
Make one.

One <u>base</u> is not there.
Fox is going to need it.
Make one.

Bear needs a <u>cap</u>.
Can you make one?

116 **Phonics Home Activity:** Have your child read the sentences and explain what he or she did on this page. Then on another sheet of paper, help your child write two or three of the underlined words without looking at them.

Read each sentence in the story. Print the
underlined word under its picture.

Duck Makes Lunch

Duck makes some <u>bread</u>.

She makes some <u>rice</u> too.

Now she makes a big <u>roast</u>.

Duck wants one big <u>plate</u>.

She finds one on the <u>shelf</u>.

Duck brings a <u>stool</u>.

She will have a nice lunch!

plate

Name _____

Read the story. Print each underlined word under its picture.

Looking for Father

Here comes the <u>train</u>.

My <u>dad</u> is on it.

It stops at the <u>fence</u>.

I am at the big <u>bush</u>.

I look for my father on the <u>stairs</u>.

I see a red hat and a red <u>shirt</u>.

They are on my father!

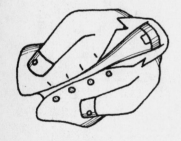

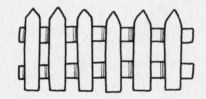

shirt

_____

_____

_____

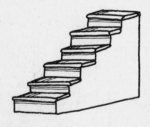

_____

_____

_____

Phonics Home Activity: Help your child read the story. Then have your child read the words at the bottom of the page and color each of the pictures.

Say each picture name. Fill in the circle
next to the word that names the picture.

★ ○ brick
   ○ truck
   ● stick

1. ○ face
   ○ fast
   ○ fresh

2. ○ tricks
   ○ tracks
   ○ trucks

3. ○ plants
   ○ shoes
   ○ cents

4. ○ plane
   ○ train
   ○ brain

5. ○ leash
   ○ list
   ○ lace

6. ○ vest
   ○ van
   ○ vase

7. ○ tree
   ○ free
   ○ stay

8. ○ stem
   ○ plum
   ○ broom

9. ○ step
   ○ sheep
   ○ trap

10. ○ stairs
    ○ shares
    ○ pliers

11. ○ cape
    ○ cap
    ○ cup

12. ○ chest
    ○ choice
    ○ cheese

13. ○ state
    ○ shirt
    ○ plant

14. ○ branch
    ○ bread
    ○ brush

Number right _____

Name _____

Read each sentence. Fill in the circle next to the picture of the underlined word.

1. Please bring me a <u>brick</u>.

2. I want a <u>vase</u> like that one.

3. I will put the <u>cap</u> in a box.

4. This is one <u>cent</u>.

5. Do you want this <u>plate</u>?

6. I can run to the <u>bush</u>.

7. We will bring the <u>toast</u>.

8. Where will the <u>train</u> stop?

Number right _____

Phonics Home Activity: Ask your child to read each sentence on this page and point to the picture of the underlined word. Then help your child write the words *vase, cup,* and *plate* without looking at them.

Say each picture name. Fill in the circle next to the letter that stands for the ending sound or sounds.

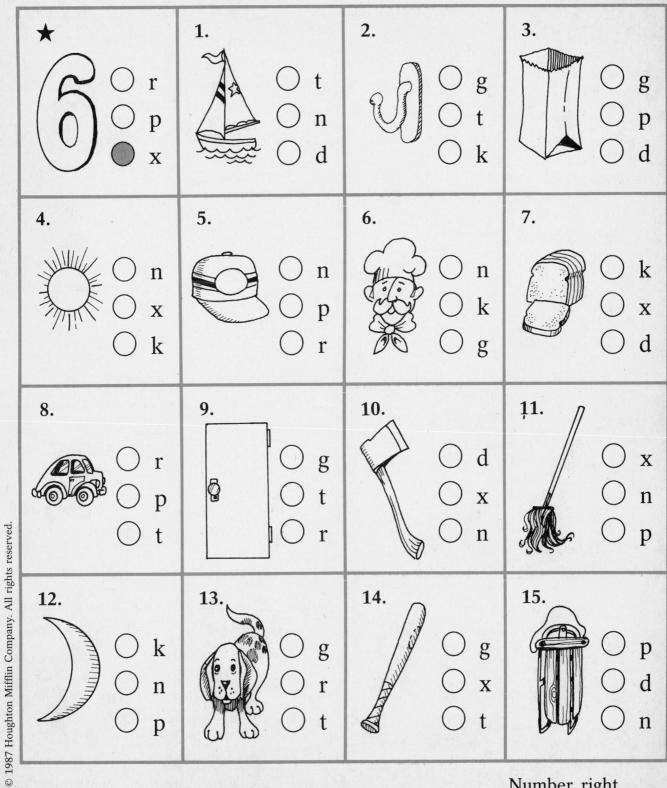

★ **6**
○ r
○ p
● x

1.
○ t
○ n
○ d

2.
○ g
○ t
○ k

3.
○ g
○ p
○ d

4.
○ n
○ x
○ k

5.
○ n
○ p
○ r

6.
○ n
○ k
○ g

7.
○ k
○ x
○ d

8.
○ r
○ p
○ t

9.
○ g
○ t
○ r

10.
○ d
○ x
○ n

11.
○ x
○ n
○ p

12.
○ k
○ n
○ p

13.
○ g
○ r
○ t

14.
○ g
○ x
○ t

15.
○ p
○ d
○ n

Number right _____

Name _____

Say each picture name. Fill in the circle next to the letters that stand for the beginning sounds.

★	1.	2.	3.
● br ○ tr ○ pl	○ fl ○ fr ○ st	○ pl ○ fl ○ tr	○ br ○ tr ○ fr

4.	5.	6.	7.
○ fr ○ fl ○ pl	○ tr ○ st ○ br	○ fr ○ br ○ tr	○ pl ○ st ○ fl

8.	9.	10.	11.
○ pl ○ br ○ st	○ fr ○ tr ○ st	○ st ○ pl ○ fl	○ st ○ br ○ fl

12.	13.	14.	15.
○ tr ○ fr ○ br	○ pl ○ fl ○ st	○ tr ○ fr ○ fl	○ fr ○ br ○ tr

Number right _____

122 **Phonics Home Activity:** Hold this page where your child can't see it, and name each picture. Ask your child to tell what letters stand for the beginning sounds of each picture name.

Say each picture name. Fill in the circle next to the
letters that stand for the beginning sound.

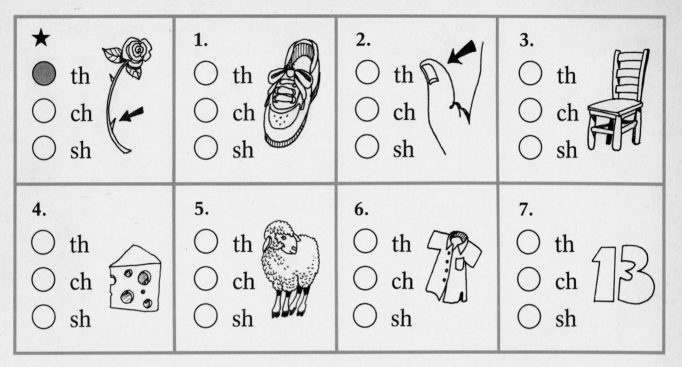

★ ● th ○ ch ○ sh

1. ○ th ○ ch ○ sh

2. ○ th ○ ch ○ sh

3. ○ th ○ ch ○ sh

4. ○ th ○ ch ○ sh

5. ○ th ○ ch ○ sh

6. ○ th ○ ch ○ sh

7. ○ th ○ ch ○ sh

Fill in the circle next to the letters that stand for
the ending sound.

★ ● th ○ ch ○ sh

8. ○ th ○ ch ○ sh

9. ○ th ○ ch ○ sh

10. ○ th ○ ch ○ sh

11. ○ th ○ ch ○ sh

12. ○ th ○ ch ○ sh

13. ○ th ○ ch ○ sh

14. ○ th ○ ch ○ sh

Number right _____

Name _____

123

Say each picture name. Fill in the circle next to the word that names the picture.

★
- ○ past
- ● paste

1.
- ○ man
- ○ mane

2.
- ○ plan
- ○ plane

3.
- ○ mat
- ○ mate

4.
- ○ tap
- ○ tape

5.
- ○ flag
- ○ flame

6.
- ○ pan
- ○ pane

7.
- ○ cap
- ○ cape

Fill in the circle next to the word that completes each sentence.

★ I am not ___ at you.
- ● mad   ○ made

8. We will ___ some lunch for you.
- ○ sat   ○ save

9. Your nose is on your ___ .
- ○ fast   ○ face

10. We will go to school in the ___ .
- ○ van   ○ vane

Number right _____

124 **Phonics Home Activity:** With a small piece of paper, cover the circles in each box at the top of this page. Have your child read and point to the word that names the picture. Then ask your child to read the completed sentences at the bottom of the page.

Sounds I Am Learning

Review	1	2	3	4		
	5	6	**7**	**8**		
Final **r/t**	9	10	11	12	13	**14**
Final **n**	15	16	17	**18**		
th	19	20	21	**22**		
Final **d/k**	23	24	25	26	27	**28**
Final **g**	29	30	31	**32**		
fl/fr	33	34	35	**36**		
Final **x**	37	38	39	40		
Final **th**	41	42	43	**44**		
Initial/Final **ch**	45	46	47	**48**		
Final **p**	49	50	51	52		
Short **a**	53	54	55	56	57	**58**
Long **a**	59	60	61	62	63	**64**

Name _____

★ The numbers on the chart are workbook page numbers.
Light numbers are practice pages.
Dark numbers are Check pages.

br	65	66	67	**68**		
tr/pl	69	70	71	**72**		
c/s/	73	74	75	**76**		
Initial/Final **st**	77	78	79	**80**		
Initial/Final **sh**	81	82	83	**84**		
Review	85	86	87	88	89	90
	91	92	**93**	**94**	95	96
	97	98	99	100	101	102
	103	**104**	105	106	107	108
	109	110	111	112	113	114
	115	116	117	118	**119**	**120**
	121	**122**	**123**	**124**		

★ The numbers on the chart are workbook page numbers.
   Light numbers are practice pages.
   Dark numbers are Check pages.